IF YOU CALL THIS INTRODUCTION "JUST AN INTRODUCTION," I'LL F***ING KILL YOU: AN INTRODUCTION BY MARK WAID

During the mid-20th century, the American advertising field was dominated by an agency known as Ogilvy & Mather, who introduced Dove Soap, Schweppes Tonic and the dream of the Rolls-Royce to American suburbia. You're almost certainly unfamiliar with O&M, but if you've ever heard the phrases "Good to the last drop" or "Don't leave home without it," you know their work.

At the height of his power, someone was stupid enough to ask co-founder David Ogilvy that one question most reviled by all creative people—"Where do you get your ideas?"—and Ogilvy gave the most perceptive answer I have ever heard:

"The best ideas start as jokes."

I am reminded of this every time I pick up anything with Garth Ennis' name on it.

In the field of comics today, Garth—and I'm not saying this just because I'm at this moment filled with bourbon and self-pity—Garth has the market cornered on humor. Oh, sure, there are creators out there who can make you laugh—or even laff—with their characters' wacky antics. There are even some of us who are known for penning dialogue full of witty, as the kids say today, "zingers." (If you've ever heard the phrases, "You can't hit what you can't see!" or "I've never seen anything so big move so fast!", you know the work of the agency Waid & Cuervo.) But Garth—like a bloodhound turning a jackrabbit into a Pollock—won't let a joke go until he's taken something cute and funny and twisted it and tortured it and transformed it into something with narrative bite. Where other writers might get one or two gags out of "Hey, imagine a guy whose head looks like a penis" or "No, no, he's got TWO hooks and TWO peg-legs!", Garth is uniquely gifted, able to subtly and inexorably turn cartoons of sophomoric humor into figures of profound horror, characters who possess the kind of depth it takes to morph some loony idea into a story with genuine power.

Meanwhile, the rest of us—like Charly, frustrated and tormented by our leaden inability to match the genius we see before us—swab our shot glasses with our tongues and pray for Garth's swift death.

Ennis' posse this time around was well-assembled. Co-creator Carlos Ezquerra beautifully interprets the sort of grotesqueries Garth can describe only in words, and an artist who can—presumably without blinking—draw a pain-in-the-ass terrier being permanently tamed by a shotgun shell has clearly found in Ennis a kindred spirit. Let's hope colorist Paul Mounts blanched just a little at what was required of him here if he ever hopes to find tenderness and true love in this world.

I don't know what else to say, really, nor should I be allowed to type given the state I'm in. Besides, any time I try to attack the keyboard after reading one of Garth's stories, I feel like a blind man in a Humvee. Read on and enjoy. If you have any further questions about the material, I'll be over here scanning the "help wanted" ads.

—Mark Waid,
Former Writer

JUST A PILGRIM #1 Variant Cover
by J.G. Jones

4

FROM THE DIARY OF
BILLY SHEPHERD,
AGED 10 1/2

EIGHT YEARS
AFTER THE
BURN

The way my Dad tells it there used to be men called
SYNTISTS who said a time wood come when the Sun
wood start to die

The Syntists said the Sun wood cool, and grow real
big, and gobble up Mercury like a snack and roast
Venus to a cinder and then it wood be OUR turn

The cities wood die SCREAMING and the
forests wood burn like HELL until The land was
desert, and the sea wood dry up and leave
what was under it for all to see

And there wood be wrecks of ships FULL of
TREASURE and GUNS for whoever was left alive to
take them, and there wood be deep deep canyons
and valleys that THINGS cood live in, things that
the rays from the dying sun had CHANGED,
and it wood be BAD to survive because
of what wood be walking the land

And my dad says the Syntists
were right about how they
said this wood happen,
except for TWO things:

5

PART ONE ANNO DOMINI

Creator/Writer:
Garth Ennis Creator/Artist:
Carlos Ezquerra

Colors:
Paul Mounts Letters:
Chris Eliopoulos Editor:
Jimmy Palmiotti

Chairman:
Gareb S. Shamus President & COO
Fred Pierce

YOU AN' ME, LORD.

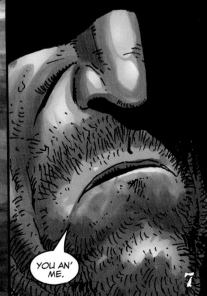

YOU AN' ME,

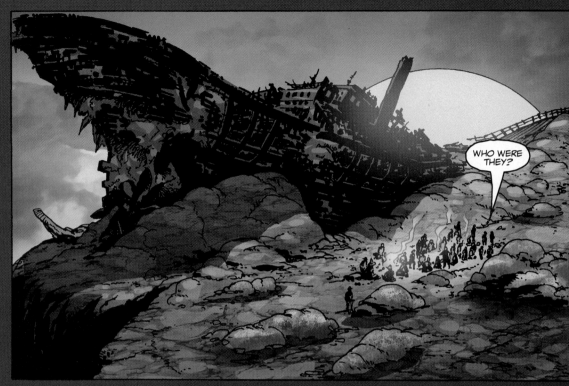

WHO WERE THEY?

BUCKERS. PIRATES. GODLESS SCUM.

SECOND PETER: THE DOG IS TURNED TO HIS OWN VOMIT AGAIN.

UH... RIGHT.

WELL, I'M JOHN SHEPHERD, THIS IS MY WIFE CARLA AND MY SON BILLY, AND THIS IS OUR GUIDE DIRK MASTERS. WE WERE HEADED FOR THE DEEP CANYONS WHEN THEY ATTACKED US; THERE'S STILL SUPPOSED TO BE WATER DOWN THERE...

OH, THERE'S WATER.

AN' THERE'S THINGS LIVIN' IN IT. THINGS IN THEM TRENCHES YOU DON'T WANNA MESS WITH. COLD AN' THE DARK GIVES 'EM SUCCOUR.

BE BETTER HEADIN' WEST BEYOND THE OL' COASTLINE, WHERE THE BEASTS O' THE LAND GOT FRIED 'FORE THE SUN COULD WARP THEIR YOUNG. UNDERGROUND THERE SHOULD BE SAFE ENOUGH.

YOU WANT, I'LL GUIDE YOU TO IT.

YOU?

AIN'T A MAN ALIVE KNOWS THE ATLANTIC FLOOR WAY I DO.

AND WHY WOULD YOU HELP US, EXACTLY?

TASK I BEEN SET.

BEEN WALKIN' THIS ACCURSED LAND THESE EIGHT YEARS SINCE THE BURN, MAKIN' WAR ON THE UNHOLY, HELPIN' LOST SHEEP FIND THEIR WAY HOME.

JUST DOIN' THE WORK O' THE LORD.

THE LORD...!

WOULDN'T YOU JUST KNOW WITH THE WORLD FRIED TO A CINDER AND HUMANITY UTTERLY SHAFTED, THERE'S STILL SOME LUNATIC DUMB ENOUGH TO BELIEVE IN--

THE FOOL HATH SAID IN HIS HEART, THERE IS NO GOD.

FOURTEENTH PSALM.

WE SHOULD DISCUSS THE GENTLEMAN'S KIND OFFER WITH THE OTHERS, DIRK.

OF COURSE NOT, DIRK.

LET'S GO AND TALK.

I'M NOT AFRAID OF THIS--

...SO THEN THINGS STARTED TO GET KIND OF SCARY, AN' DAD AN' SOME OTHERS DECIDED TO START OVER DOWN IN THE CANYONS...

WELL, THEY GOT THEMSELVES A MITE OFF-COURSE, BOY. YOU WERE HEADED DUE SOUTH WHEN I PICKED UP YORE TRAIL.

HOW YOU MEAN, KIND OF SCARY?

I DUNNO, IT--

IT WAS LIKE THE SETTLEMENT JUST WENT *BAD.* THERE WASN'T ENOUGH FOOD TO GO AROUND, AN' PEOPLE WERE KILLIN' EACH OTHER OVER CANS OF SOUP, AN' NO-ONE TRUSTED ANYONE.

THERE WAS EVEN ONE MAN THEY SAID ATE *HIS FAMILY...*

HIS SKIN GO YELLOW?

HUH?

EATIN' HUMAN FLESH TURNS YORE SKIN YELLOW, FIRST SIGN O' CANNIBALISM.

HOW D'YOU KNOW A THING LIKE THAT, MISTER?

I JUST KNOW.

21

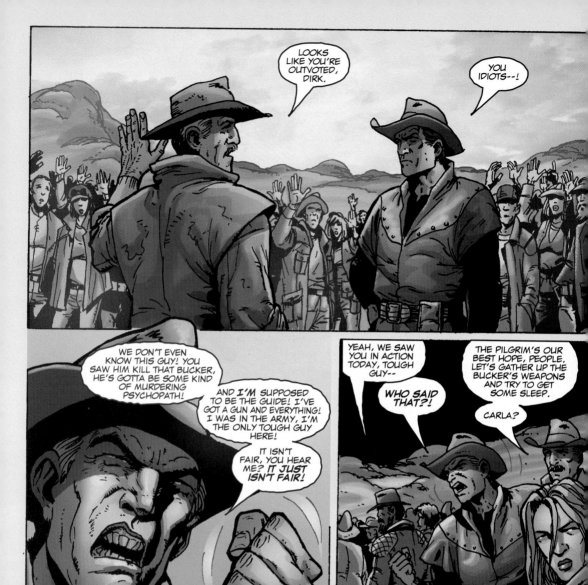

LOOKS LIKE YOU'RE OUTVOTED, DIRK.

YOU IDIOTS--!

WE DON'T EVEN KNOW THIS GUY! YOU SAW HIM KILL THAT BUCKER, HE'S GOTTA BE SOME KIND OF MURDERING PSYCHOPATH!

AND I'M SUPPOSED TO BE THE GUIDE! I'VE GOT A GUN AND EVERYTHING! I WAS IN THE ARMY, I'M THE ONLY TOUGH GUY HERE!

IT ISN'T FAIR, YOU HEAR ME? IT JUST ISN'T FAIR!

YEAH, WE SAW YOU IN ACTION TODAY, TOUGH GUY--

WHO SAID THAT?!

THE PILGRIM'S OUR BEST HOPE, PEOPLE. LET'S GATHER UP THE BUCKER'S WEAPONS AND TRY TO GET SOME SLEEP.

CARLA?

... THERE'S SOMETHING ABOUT THAT MAN.

I CAN'T HELP THINKING I'VE SEEN HIM BEFORE...

YIP!
YIP!
YIP!

YIP!
YIP!
YIP!

WHAT IS THAT?

THAT'S OLD MRS. KENNING'S DOG JO-JO. SHE WENT CRAZY AN' WANDERED OFF ONE NIGHT, NO-ONE EVER SAW HER AGAIN.

BUT WE KIND OF GOT USED TO JO-JO...

SO HOW FAR DO YOU THINK WE'LL GET TODAY, SIR?

YIP--

DEVIL GOT INTO HIM.

LUCKY I SAW IT IN TIME.

YIP! YIP!
YIP! YIP!

23

C-CAP'N?

AYE...?

REAVER PATROL'S DUE IN AT DAWN, CAP'N. DUNNO THE DETAILS, BUT IT SEEMS LIKE SOMEONE... UH... FOUGHT BACK...

FOUGHT BACK AN' *BEAT'EM*, AS A MATTERA FACT.

AYE.

SO THERE'S ONE OUT THERE WHO'LL STAND AGAINST YE, IS THERE, CASTENADO...?

ONE WHO'LL... MAKE A FIGHT OF IT...?

OH WELL.

OH WELL.

YE ALWAYS KNEW THIS DAY WOULD COME...

≫ TO BE CONTINUED ≪

29

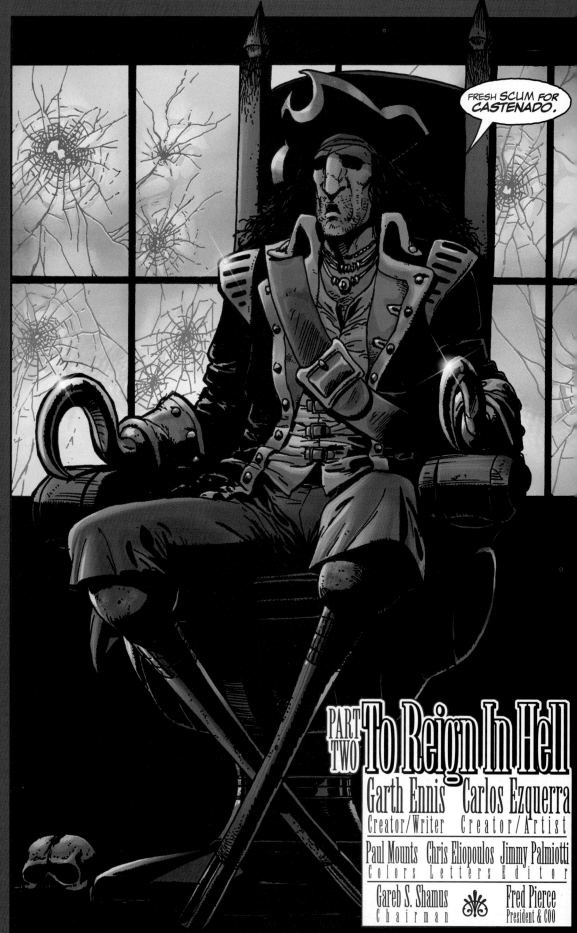

AAAAAH! AAAAAAAHH!!

HE'S BEEN *CHANGED*, SEE. THEM RAYS COMIN' OUTTA THE SUN NOWADAYS, THEY DONE STUFF TO HIS SENSES. NO EYES, NO, BUT HE CAN HEAR A PIN DROP A MILE AWAY, AN' SNIFF OUT A RUNNIN' MAN FROM THE *FEAR* GETS LEFT IN THE AIR...

WAY CASTENADO SEES YOU--

AAAAAAAHH!!

--YOU'RE A RADAR BLIP ON HIS SOUL.

CAPTAIN CASTENADO, AH, WE'D LIKE TO JOIN YOUR ORGANIZATION RIGHT AWAY--

WE'RE YOUR MEN, SIR! BLOODY BUCKERS, THAT'S US!

I CAN UNDERSTAND YOUR ENTHUSIASM, ME PAIR O' EAGER PUPS... FOR WHEN THE *BURN* DRIED UP THE SEAS, I GOT WIND O' THE *HELL* LEFT BEHIND-- AN' BETTER TO REIGN THERE THAN SERVE ABOVE, IS WHAT I SAID TO MESELF...

RIGHT ON!

AN' WHEN I STUMBLED ON THIS MIGHTY VESSEL SETTLED TO THE SEABED, BRISTLIN' WI' ITS ORDINANCE, I KNEW WHICH WAY'D BE FOR ME...

BUT HAVE YE IT *IN YE*, LADS? COULD 'E PASS CERTAIN *TESTS*, WERE THEY SET THEM?

COULD YOU CHEW THE LIPS FROM A DEAD MAN'S FACE, OR WEAR A NECKLACE O' DONGS? PUT NINE TIMES NINE STEEL NAILS THROUGH YER SKIN? KILL INFANTS STILL AT THE TEAT?

TAKE A *GOAT*, COULD YE, THOUGH THERE BE THIRTY MEN IN THE LINE AHEAD A YE, AN' THE POOR BEAST'S NETHERS BE MUSH...?

YOU'RE OUT OF YOUR TINY MIND! I'M NOT DOING ANYTHING TO A GOAT!

I MEAN--

OH DEAR.

AAAAlllIEEEEE!!

AN' WHO IS IT'S *OUT THERE*, CASTENADO...?

WHO... MIGHT... IT... *BE*...

AAAAAAAHH!!
AAAAAAAHH!!
AAAAAAAHH!!

SO IT DOESN'T KILL YOU, YOU SAID? IT *MATES* WITH YOU?

KILLS TO PROTECT ITS HELLISH BROOD. GOTTA HOPE THINGS AIN'T GOT THAT FAR.

THIS HERE'S OUR WAY IN...

WELL. YOU AN' ME, LORD.

YOU AN' ME.

HOW COME THE FLOOR'S SO SOFT IN HERE?

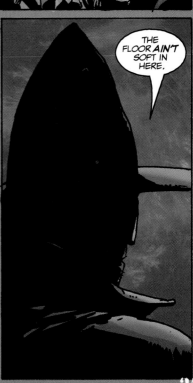

THE FLOOR *AIN'T* SOFT IN HERE.

RRRRIIIIIEE

RRRRIIIIIEEEEEEEEEE

NOW, CREATURE--

HIS WRATH IS UPON YOU!

RRRRIIIII

GO BACK TO PERDITION, SPAWN OF HELL!!

WHERE ARE McCARTHY AND CURTISS?

McCARTHY AND CURTISS ARE DEAD.

I DON'T WANT TO TALK ABOUT IT.

WHAT ABOUT DIRK...?

DIRK WE GOT. KEEP HAULIN', BOYS.

WHAT THE HELL-- IS THIS--

WAY THAT DAMN THING REPRODUCES IS, IT USES A LIVIN' HOST TO CARRY ITS YOUNG TO TERM. PUMPS IN ITS EVIL SEED AN' LEAVES 'EM TO INCUBATE.

WHICH CAUSES CERTAIN CHANGES IN THE HOST, O' COURSE.

TIME WE GOT TO OL' DIRK, THE BEAST ALREADY HAD ITS WICKED WAY...

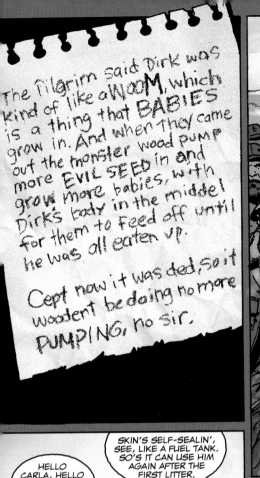

The Pilgrim said Dirk was kind of like a WOOM, which is a thing that BABIES grow in. And when they came out the monster wood pump more EVIL SEED in and grow more babies, with Dirk's body in the middel for them to feed off until he was all eaten up.

Cept now it was ded, so it woodent be doing no more PUMPING, no sir.

So really Dirk was quite lucky.

SEE THE YOUNG MOVIN' ROUND INSIDE THERE?

...NOT HAPPENING, NOT TO ME. I'M THE HERO AROUND HERE, I'M JUST HAVING A NIGHTMARE, THAT'S ALL...

HELLO CARLA, HELLO BILLY, ARE YOU IN MY DREAM TOO?

SKIN'S SELF-SEALIN', SEE, LIKE A FUEL TANK. SO'S IT CAN USE HIM AGAIN AFTER THE FIRST LITTER.

LOOKS LIKE THEM LITTLE DEMONS'RE GITTIN' READY TO POP...

SO...SO WHAT ARE WE GOING TO DO...?

THAT'S ENOUGH!

I DON'T CARE WHO YOU ARE, I WON'T HAVE YOU FILLING MY BILLY'S HEAD WITH YOUR FIRE-AND-BRIMSTONE CRAP!

WHAT THE HELL ARE YOU THINKING, ANYWAY? GIVING A LITTLE BOY NIGHTMARES! TRAUMATIZING HIM!

WELL MA'AM, WHICH IS WORSE:

SCARIN' THE TRUTH INTO THE CHILD?

OR TELLIN' HIM THERE AIN'T NO GOD?

IT'S-- A DREAM-- A DREEEEEAAMM--!

HMMPH!

CARLA, BE REASONABLE! I MEAN HE SAVED DIRK! HE SAVED BILLY, FOR GOODNESS' SAKE!

I DON'T CARE WHA' HE DID. I DON'T LI' THAT MAN, I DON' LIKE THAT BILLY LIKES HIM.

AND I KNOW I'VE SEEN HIM BEFORE, SOMEWHERE...

THAT'S THEM, CAP'N!

AYE... AYE, I SMELL 'EM ...'AN I SMELL *HIM* DOWN THERE...

GOT THE SCENT O' *MAD AN' BLOODY DEATH* UPON HIM, HE HAS...

I'LL CALL BLACKHEART BASE, CAP'N!

OH GOD, THEY'VE FOUND US...!

CAN'T WE SHOOT THEM DOWN?

THEY'RE TOO HIGH, SHEPHERD! THEY CAN JUST SIT UP THERE AND GUIDE THEIR PALS RIGHT ONTO US!

NO-ONE COULD HIT THEM AT THAT RANGE!

I RECKON NOT.

45

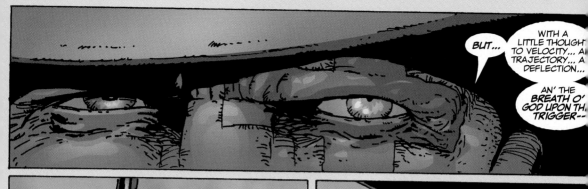

BUT... WITH A LITTLE THOUGHT TO VELOCITY... A TRAJECTORY... A DEFLECTION...

AN' THE *BREATH O' GOD* UPON TH' TRIGGER--

GO AHEAD, REAVER NINE--

BASE, WE *GOT* THE BASTARDS! SCRAMBLE THE GUNBOATS TO GRID REF-

JESUS!!

47

53

FROM THE DIARY OF BILLY SHEPHERD, AGED 10 1/2

When we found out what the Pilgrim had done before the burn, pretty much everyone but my Dad and me wanted to kill him strate away.

But Dad said he saved our lives, so he was entiteld to a fair trial and we shood at least let him speak in his own defens. DIRK said how cood we trust him to tell the truth, cause he wood just skip the really bad bits?

Cept once he got started, if he DID leave any of it out, I think peepel were probly GLAD.

I GUESS THE TROUBLE BEGAN WHEN I GOT ME A TASTE FER HUMAN FLESH...

PART THREE:

BLOODY BASKETS

Garth Ennis Creator/Writer   Carlos Ezquerra Creator/Artist   Paul Mounts Colors   Chris Eliopoulos Letters   Jimmy Palmiotti Editor

Gareb S. Shamus Chairman   Fred Pierce President & COO

SEE, IT'S ONE THING TO DO IT WHEN YOU AIN'T GOT NO CHOICE, WHEN IT'S JUST A MATTER O' SURVIVAL. BUT YOU START KILLIN' AN' EATIN' FOLKS 'CAUSE YOU LIKE IT...

WELL, THAT DON'T GO DOWN TOO WELL IN MOST QUARTERS, NO SIR.

I CAN'T BELIEVE WE'RE LISTENING TO THIS! THE GUY'S A *CANNIBAL*-- WHAT THE HELL'S HIS EXCUSE FOR *THAT* GOING TO BE?

I MEAN WHAT THE HELL ARE WE WAITING FOR, THE BIT WHERE WE ALL GO, OH, WELL, THAT'S PERFECTLY UNDERSTANDABLE! *THERE BUT FOR THE GRACE OF GOD GO I!*

AFTER ALL, WE'VE ALL BEEN THERE, HAVEN'T WE? "GOD, IF ONLY THERE WAS SOMETHING *OTHER THAN PIZZA*..."

AT LEAST HEAR HIM OUT, DIRK! HE RESCUED YOU FROM THAT... *THING*, DIDN'T HE?

I GOT *RAPED BY A GIANT SQUID*, SHEPHERD! HIM SHOOTING IT AFTERWARDS DOES *NOT* CONSTITUTE A RESCUE!

I woodent have felt SORRY for him.

Rite then I looked at him and KNEW he woodent go on talking, or ask for quiet, or beg for mercy, or show any weekness EVER.

And I guess if he did do those things--

LET HIM SPEAK!

55

Cause then he woodent have been HIM.

ER...

BACK IN THE TIME BEFORE THE BURN I WAS A SOLDIER.

"GOOD ONE, TOO. ME AN' THE MEN O' MY COMMAND, WE DID THE WORK THAT OTHERS COULDN'T DO. *NO JOB TOO CRAZY,* S'WHAT WE LIKED TO SAY.

"FOUR O' US FOUGHT EVERYWHERE FROM SLOBODAN'SK TO SAN FRANCISCO, KILLED BLACK WIDOW AGUILERA IN HER PALACE, GOT CAUGHT ONE TIME ON A HILLTOP NORTH O' ELIAN CITY: WALKED DOWN OFF THAT SUM'BITCH PAST THIRTEEN HUNDRED DEAD CUBANOS, BARRELS ON THE SHRAPGUNS WORN SMOOTH."

57

CAME THE DAY THE SQUAD WAS BOUND FOR TINIAN IN THE PACIFIC, ON A *HALO* DROP TO HIT THE BRANCH ENOLAN DISSIDENTS, AN' A STORM AROSE THAT FLUNG US FROM OUR COURSE.

"FIVE HOURS WE SPENT, BOILIN', CHURNIN', CAUGHT FAST WITHIN THE BELLY O' THE MAELSTROM--"

AAAAAGGGHH!!

CHUTE UP AN' STAND READY, SHE WON'T TAKE MUCH MORE OF THIS! SOMEONE GO CHECK ON THE CREW!

YOU GOT IT, MAJOR!

EMERGENCY ONLY LIFE RAFT

THE FRIGGIN' CREW'S EJECTED!

COWARDLY SCUM--!

GO, BOYS!!

GO! GO! GO!

"WEREN'T NONE BUT US COULD MAKE A JUMP LIKE THAT. TO THIS DAY STILL, I DON'T RECALL THE PARTICULARS OF THAT DESCENT."

"BUT MAKE IT WE DID, AN' BY THE WILL O' GOD..."

"WHOSE HAND, O' COURSE, IS IN ALL THINGS."

BOYS, I WON'T LIE TO YOU: WE'RE IN A TIGHT SPOT. STUCK IN THE MIDDLE O' THE OCEAN, NO FOOD, MINIMAL WATER, NO WAY TO CALL FOR HELP. BUT AM I DOWNHEARTED...?

AM I HELL!

WE ARE THE *VERY BEST*, BOYS! WE ARE ASSKICKERS AN' LIFETAKERS! NO JOB TOO CRAZY, GODDAMN, IF *ANYONE* CAN COME THROUGH THIS IT IS *US*!

DIDN'T WE JUST SKYDIVE THROUGH A HURRICANE? DIDN'T WE STAY IN CONTACT THE WHOLE WAY DOWN? WE SURVIVED THAT BY *SKILL*, *TEAMWORK* AN' *TRUST*, JUST LIKE ALWAYS-- AN' *BY GOD* THAT IS HOW WE WILL SURVIVE *THIS*!

LEMME HEAR IT *LOUD*, BOYS...!

GODDAMN RIGHT!!

59

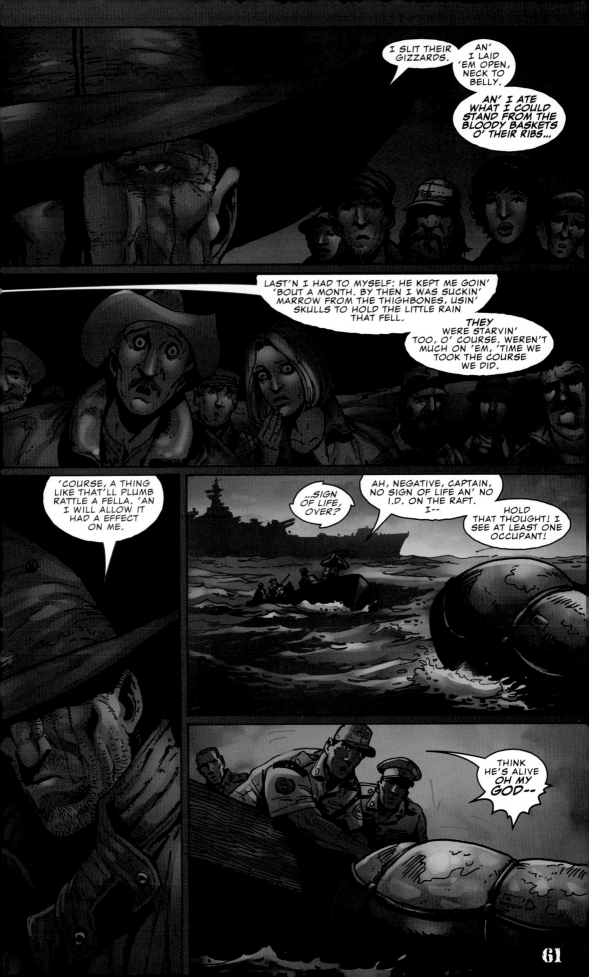

I SLIT THEIR GIZZARDS.

AN' I LAID 'EM OPEN, NECK TO BELLY.

AN' I ATE WHAT I COULD STAND FROM THE BLOODY BASKETS O' THEIR RIBS...

LAST'N I HAD TO MYSELF: HE KEPT ME GOIN' 'BOUT A MONTH. BY THEN I WAS SUCKIN' MARROW FROM THE THIGHBONES, USIN' SKULLS TO HOLD THE LITTLE RAIN THAT FELL.

THEY WERE STARVIN' TOO, O' COURSE. WEREN'T MUCH ON 'EM, 'TIME WE TOOK THE COURSE WE DID.

'COURSE, A THING LIKE THAT'LL PLUMB RATTLE A FELLA. 'AN I WILL ALLOW IT HAD A EFFECT ON ME.

...SIGN OF LIFE, OVER?

AH, NEGATIVE, CAPTAIN, NO SIGN OF LIFE AN' NO I.D. ON THE RAFT. I--

HOLD THAT THOUGHT! I SEE AT LEAST ONE OCCUPANT!

THINK HE'S ALIVE OH MY GOD--

SO-- SO YOU WENT HOME AND JUST-- KEPT AT IT?

NO. 'TIME I GOT OUTTA THE HOSPITAL, WORD'D GOT AROUND THE REGIMENT. WASN'T ANYONE REAL KEEN ON SERVIN' WITH ME, OR EVEN LOOKIN' AT ME.

GAVE ME A PSYCH DISCHARGE AN' I TURNED TO THE BOTTLE AGAIN, WORSE'N EVER BEFORE...

I'D'VE BEEN ON BACK THE INSTANT I WAS OFF THE RAFT...

WASN'T THE RAFT, MA'AM. THAT DIDN'T BOTHER ME BACK THEN-- 'LEAST NOT SO I COULD TELL RIGHT AWAY. I DONE WHAT I HAD TO DO TO SURVIVE AN' NOW I WAS READY TO GET BACK TO WORK.

I DRANK 'CAUSE THEY THREW ME OUTTA THE ARMY, WHICH WAS THE ONLY HOME I EVER HAD.

"BUT ONE NIGHT I WAS DRIVIN' BACK FROM A TAVERN I FREQUENTED..."

JESHUSH CHRISHT!

"SOME OL' HOBO FELLA, NEVER EVEN KNEW WHAT HIT HIM."

"THE STREET WAS EMPTY, AN' EVEN WITH THE RAIN THE NIGHT WAS STILL, STOOD THERE A LONG TIME, ALL BUT HYPNOTIZED, GAZIN' DOWN UPON THAT LIFELESS SHELL..."

HE LOOKED A LITTLE...

KINDA...

UNDERDONE.

"I FIXED THAT RIGHT AWAY."

...SO THE BIBLE'S TRUE 'CAUSE IT SAYS SO IN THE BIBLE; THAT IT? I THINK I GOT A BRIDGE I CAN SELL YOU, FATHER.

HEH.

IT'S TRUE BECAUSE YOU *FEEL* IT'S TRUE, MY FRIEND. BECAUSE YOU BELIEVE AND ACCEPT IT IN YOUR HEART.

PEOPLE GO LOOKING FOR GOD *OUTSIDE*-- FOR PROOF, FOR SIGNS OF HIS EXISTANCE IN THE MATERIAL WORLD-- WHEN REALLY THEY SHOULD BE LOOKING INSIDE.

IN *HERE.*

AN' GOD'S INSIDE YOU, FATHER?

HE IS.

AN' YORE CERTAIN O' THAT? YOU DON'T DOUBT, YOU DON'T QUESTION-- YOU KIN GO ON AN' DO WHAT YORE S'POSED TO, AN' HE'LL TAKE CARE O' THE REST?

HE WILL.

WHY DO YOU ASK...?

JUST THINKIN'.

SEEMS A LITTLE BIT LIKE THE ARMY.

NEXT WEEK, THEN.

EXCEPT THERE WEREN'T NO NEXT WEEK.
THERE WAS JUST THE BURN.
"THAT FIRST DAY, IT WAS LIKE THE SKY WAS SET AFIRE.
WH-WH-WHAT IS IT, FATHER?
"TO THEM THAT AWAITED ARMAGEDDON, IT SEEMED THAT TIME HAD COME."

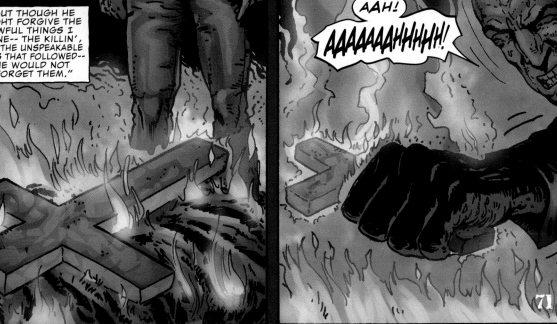

AN' SO I SET OUT INTO WHAT WAS LEFT O' THE WORLD, INTENT ON DOIN' THE LORD'S WORK. ON A DIFFERENT JOURNEY NOW, BUT... STILL JUST A PILGRIM.

"AS A FIREBRAND PLUCKED OUT O' THE BURNIN'."

AMOS.

CHAPTER FOUR, VERSE ELEVEN.

MY.

ASS.

NOW WAIT A MINUTE, DIRK--

OH COME ON, YOU'RE NOT TELLING ME YOU *BUY THAT*, ARE YOU? A QUICK READ OF HIS BIBLE AND A BIT OF SELF-MUTILATION AND EVERYTHING'S JUST JIM-DANDY?

WELL NO, BUT-- BUT HOW DO YOU JUDGE A THING LIKE THAT? I MEAN WHAT HE MUST HAVE GONE THROUGH ON THAT RAFT--!

HE'S *STILL* OUR ONLY HOPE OF CROSSING THE ATLANTIC FLOOR...

PISS OFF, SHEPHERD! THE SOONER WE KILL THIS LUNATIC THE BETTER!

IT'S THEM! THE BUCKERS!

WE'RE UNDER ATTACK!

B-B-BUCKERS--!

FROM THE DIARY OF BILLY SHEPHERD, AGED 10 1/2

Dad cut the Pilgrim loose just as quick as you ever did see— but once the BUCKERS hit us, what good even HE COOD do seemed kind of DOWTFUL—

AAAAAIIIIEEEE!

Part Four:

FIRESTARTER

Garth Ennis Creator/Writer   **Carlos Ezquerra** Creator/Artist   Paul Mounts Colors   Chris Eliopoulos Letters   Jimmy Palmiotti Editor

Gareb S. Shamus Chairman   Fred Pierce President & COO

ON, ME BLOODY BUCKERS... ON, ON...

INTO THE FIGHT FOR YER CAP'N, AYE, AN' BY DAWN WE'LL DANCE ON THESE CRAVEN CURS' *BONES*...

WE HAVEN'T A CHANCE HERE! THAT NAPALM LAUNCHER'S KILLING US!

WHAT THE HELL ARE *YOU* LOOKING AT?

ANGLERJACK.

ONE O' THE BIGGER MOLEFISH. BURROWER. LIKES TO LAY IN AMBUSH, DRAG PREY INTO ITS NEST.

YEAH? AND WHAT DOES *IT* DO TO YOU? DOES IT BLOW YOUR GENITALS UP LIKE BALLOONS AND USE THEM FOR SIGHTSEEING TRIPS?

IT DIGS TUNNELS.

GIVE ME YORE PISTOL, SHEPHERD.

BILLY, GET DOWN--!

BUT I WANNA *SEE*, MOM!

SCREW *THIS*--

DIRK, NO! IT'S DEATH OUT THERE, YOU FOOL!

UNNH--!

YOU AN' ME, LORD.

YOU AN' ME.

79

NO-- GET HIM-- *AAAIIIEEEE!*

AAAAAH--!

THAT SMELL... THAT *STENCH* AGAIN, O' DEAD MEN'S BLOOD ON MADMAN'S BREATH...

STOP HIM, ME BUCKERS! KILL THAT DEVIL O' HELL!

THERE!

WHO CAN COUNT THE DUST O' JACOB, AN' THE NUMBER O' THE FOURTH PART O' ISRAEL?

LET ME DIE THE DEATH O' THE RIGHTEOUS--

HOLY JESUS!

WE CAN'T FIGHT THAT, CAP'N! RUN!

AYE...

BUT MARK ME, MATEY... MARK ME, NOW... YE'VE THE CURSE O' CASTENADO UPON YER HEAD...

AN' YER TIME IS COMIN' SOON.

WELL, NOW.

THINKIN' O' LEAVIN' US, BOY...?

EVERYONE HERE? WHO'S HURT, IS ANYONE--

MAN, DID YOU SEE THOSE SCUMBAGS RUN?

THEY'LL BE BACK.

BEST WE GIT MOVIN'.

REST KIN WAIT 'TIL LATER.

WHAT A NIGHT...

YEAH, I SURE LIKED BUCKIN' BETTER WHEN THE BUCKEES DIDN'T BUCK BACK...

MOSTA THE WOUNDED WON'T LAST THE DAY, CAP'N. THAT NAPALM'S EVIL STUFF.

CALL THE CARRIER, AYE. HAVE 'EM SEN UP THE REST C THE BOYS, AN EVERY MACHIN THAT'LL RUN.

WE'RE GOIN' ON? BUT THE FIRST GOOD WIND'LL BLOW THEIR TRACKS OUT--

WE'RE GOIN' ON.

LET THAT BE THE END O' IT, LAD, OR YE'LL FEEL MY HOOK IN YER POOPCHUTE...

THEM PRISONERS WE TOOK, CAP'N-- THE FOOLS GOT LOST IN THE SMOKE?

AYE...?

WE GOT ONE SAYS HE KNOWS WHAT COURSE THEM MAGGOTS'RE TAKIN', CAP'N. SAYS HE CAN LEAD US RIGHT ONTO 'EM--

SO LONG AS WE LET HIM LIVE.

Without the Transport the Buckers run off and left we woodent have stood a chance. We knew theyd still come looking for us - but the Pilgrim was good as his word.

He knew the secret ways throgh the ATLANTIC RIDGE MOUNTENS, which wood take the Buckers AGES to find...

He knew where other travelers had stashed FOOD and GAS, to help folks mite one day be traveling those same ways...

Not a man alive knows the Atlantic flor the way HE does.

On the plains beyond the mountens we made real good time. We drove as long as it WAS lite-- which is longer now than before the burn, Dad says, because the sun is so much closer to the earth. Sometimes we drove by moonlight too.

Ten days we headed west.

Fifteen.

Then came the night we saw the WHALES.

85

IT was a strange, SAD place.

IT made you feel like you cood get down in the dust between the bones and CRY FOREVER.

Mom said later it was kind of reminder what had hapend to the WORLD—cause no matter where we went or how hard we fot, things wood never, EVER be the same.

There was no going back for any of us.

But I had a REAL bad time that nite.

I started seeing EYES inside the sockets of the skulls, and giant GHOSTS that rose up off the skeletons and tried and tried to swim away but COODENT...

And I thot I cood hear WHISPERS out there, not voices like we have—but full of so much pain I thot my heart wood DIE.

DON'T LET 'EM SCARE YOU, BILLY.

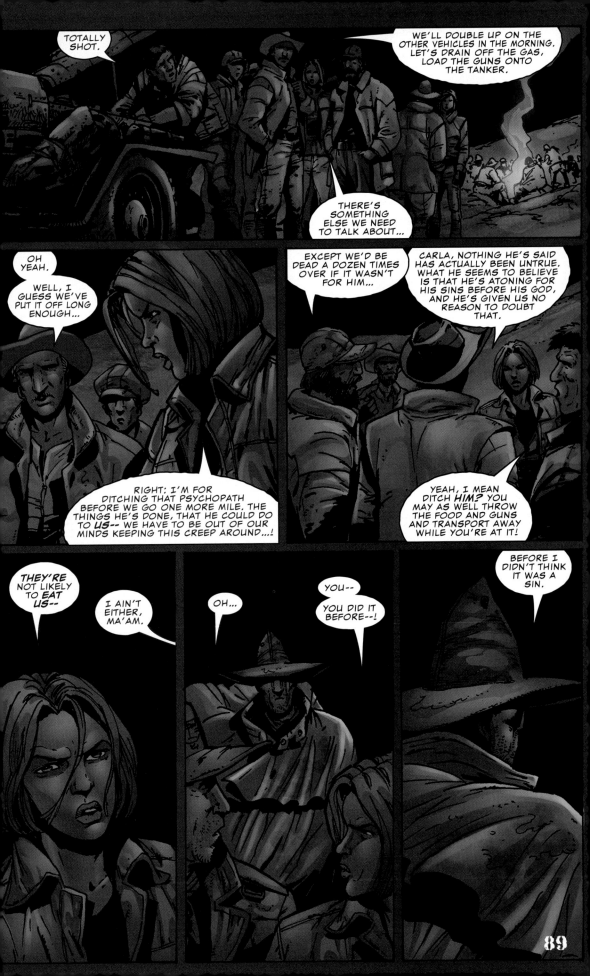

TOTALLY SHOT.

WE'LL DOUBLE UP ON THE OTHER VEHICLES IN THE MORNING. LET'S DRAIN OFF THE GAS, LOAD THE GUNS ONTO THE TANKER.

THERE'S SOMETHING ELSE WE NEED TO TALK ABOUT...

OH YEAH.

WELL, I GUESS WE'VE PUT IT OFF LONG ENOUGH...

EXCEPT WE'D BE DEAD A DOZEN TIMES OVER IF IT WASN'T FOR HIM...

CARLA, NOTHING HE'S SAID HAS ACTUALLY BEEN UNTRUE. WHAT HE SEEMS TO BELIEVE IS THAT HE'S ATONING FOR HIS SINS BEFORE HIS GOD, AND HE'S GIVEN US NO REASON TO DOUBT THAT.

RIGHT: I'M FOR DITCHING THAT PSYCHOPATH BEFORE WE GO ONE MORE MILE. THE THINGS HE'S DONE, THAT HE COULD DO TO US-- WE HAVE TO BE OUT OF OUR MINDS KEEPING THIS CREEP AROUND...!

YEAH, I MEAN DITCH HIM? YOU MAY AS WELL THROW THE FOOD AND GUNS AND TRANSPORT AWAY WHILE YOU'RE AT IT!

THEY'RE NOT LIKELY TO EAT US--

I AIN'T EITHER, MA'AM.

OH...

YOU-- YOU DID IT BEFORE--!

BEFORE I DIDN'T THINK IT WAS A SIN.

89

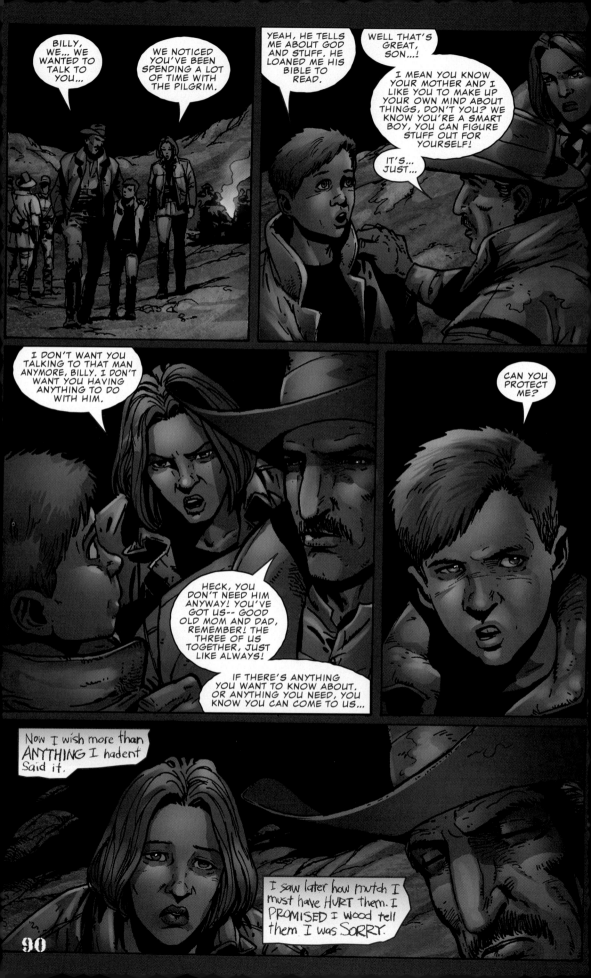

BILLY, WE... WE WANTED TO TALK TO YOU...

WE NOTICED YOU'VE BEEN SPENDING A LOT OF TIME WITH THE PILGRIM.

YEAH, HE TELLS ME ABOUT GOD AND STUFF. HE LOANED ME HIS BIBLE TO READ.

WELL THAT'S GREAT, SON...!

I MEAN YOU KNOW YOUR MOTHER AND I LIKE YOU TO MAKE UP YOUR OWN MIND ABOUT THINGS, DON'T YOU? WE KNOW YOU'RE A SMART BOY, YOU CAN FIGURE STUFF OUT FOR YOURSELF!

IT'S... JUST...

I DON'T WANT YOU TALKING TO THAT MAN ANYMORE, BILLY, I DON'T WANT YOU HAVING ANYTHING TO DO WITH HIM.

HECK, YOU DON'T NEED HIM ANYWAY! YOU'VE GOT US-- GOOD OLD MOM AND DAD, REMEMBER! THE THREE OF US TOGETHER, JUST LIKE ALWAYS!

IF THERE'S ANYTHING YOU WANT TO KNOW ABOUT, OR ANYTHING YOU NEED, YOU KNOW YOU CAN COME TO US...

CAN YOU PROTECT ME?

Now I wish more than ANYTHING I hadent said it.

I saw later how mutch I must have HURT them. I PROMISED I wood tell them I was SORRY.

90

OH GOD... OH GOD, THEY'LL BRING THE OTHERS DOWN ON US...

THAT THEY WILL.

GUESS THIS IS AS FAR AS WE GO.

AH... COME AGAIN?

VEHICLES'RE FINISHED. NO WAY WE'LL OUTRUN 'EM NOW.

LAST STAND?

THIS IS AS GOOD A PLACE FER A LAST STAND AS I EVER SAW.

LOOK, WE'RE NOT MAKING ANY KIND OF STAND! WE'RE OUTNUMBERED TWENTY TO ONE, WE'RE TOTALLY OUTGUNNED! WE'LL ALL GET BLOODY SLAUGHTERED!

GONNA HAPPEN FER CERTAIN, Y'ALL DON'T MAKE A FIGHT O' IT.

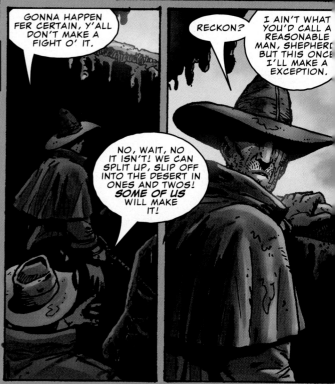

RECKON?

I AIN'T WHAT YOU'D CALL A REASONABLE MAN, SHEPHERD, BUT THIS ONCE I'LL MAKE A EXCEPTION.

NO, WAIT, NO IT ISN'T! WE CAN SPLIT UP, SLIP OFF INTO THE DESERT IN ONES AND TWOS! *SOME OF US* WILL MAKE IT!

WE'LL LET FOLKS DECIDE FER THEMSELVES.

YOU PEOPLE KNOW WHAT'S GONNA HAPPEN WHEN THEM SCUM COME BACK HERE. NOW WHAT KINDA CHANCE YOU GOT IF YOU SURRENDER.

AN' YOU KNOW *ME*-- AN' WHATEVER ELSE YOU THINK O' ME, YOU KNOW I WILL NOT LIE TO YOU.

YOU FOLKS ARE SCARED, I UNDERSTAND THAT. SOME O' YOU ARE READY TO DESPAIR. I HAVE HEARD YOU TALKIN' ROUND YORE CAMPFIRES, ASKIN' WHAT REASON THERE IS FER GOIN' ON-- WHAT HOPE THERE IS TO LIVE FER, IN A DRIED-UP, WASTED WORLD LIKE THIS'N.

AN' SO I SAY TO YOU, HAVE FAITH! WHAT YOU CAN'T UNDERSTAND, WHERE YOU KIN SEE NO PURPOSE, SURRENDER YORE MIND AN' SOUL TO THE LORD!

ACCEPT THAT *HE* HAS A PLAN! THAT THOUGH IT MAY NOT BE CLEAR TO YOU NOW, ALL WILL BE REVEALED UPON THE DAY O' JUDGEMENT! MAKE *GOD* YORE REASON TO GO ON--

MAKE *FAITH* YORE HOPE TO LIVE FER!

SO CONSIDER THE CHOICE THAT LIES BEFORE YOU! ASK YORESELVES-- YOU WANNA DIE LIKE ANIMALS, HUNTED THROUGH THE WILDERNESS? LIKE THE DAMNED AN' FORSAKEN, BEGGIN' ON YORE KNEES FER MERCY THAT KIN NEVER COME?

OR YOU WANNA TAKE A CHANCE ON STANDIN' TALL AN' *FIGHTIN'* FER YORE LIVES? ON GOIN' TO MEET YORE MAKER SURE O' YORE HUMANITY-- AN' SURE O' YORE *IMMORTAL SOUL?!*

95

ER... I CAN'T PRETEND TO BE AS GOOD A LEADER AS THE PILGRIM... I CAN'T EVEN PRETEND TO SPEAK AS WELL AS HE HAS...

NOW I KNOW I'VE DEFENDED HIM BEFORE, BUT THINK ABOUT WHAT HE'S SAYING TO YOU, OKAY?

YOU CAN'T LET HIM, HIS, HIS *POWER* BLIND YOU TO THAT. PEOPLE, YOU HAVE GOT TO THINK FOR YOURSELVES HERE, I REALLY CAN'T EMPHASIZE THAT ENOUGH...

THESE WORDS HE'S USING, LIKE *FAITH* AND *HOPE* AND *HUMANITY* AND *STANDING TALL*-- THEY SOUND GOOD, I KNOW, BUT WHAT THEY ACTUALLY MEAN IS *DEATH*. TOTALLY, BLOODY, NIGHTMARISH, INESCAPABLE DEATH...

REMEMBER WHEN WE STARTED OUT? WHEN WE LEFT THE SETTLEMENT AT FAROE?

WE HAD A PLAN THEN, TO FIND A NEW HOME AND START OVER-- AND WE CAN STILL MAKE THAT HAPPEN, PEOPLE! SOME OF US CAN GET AWAY-- MAYBE MOST OF US, IF WE'RE CLEVER ABOUT IT!

THINGS NEEDN'T BE AS *ABSOLUTE* AS HE SAYS...!

SHEPHERD?

YOU'RE A GOOD MAN, SHEPHERD.

BUT THE WORLD YOU BELONG TO IS PASSED AWAY.

YE'VE A CHANCE TO DO THIS PEACEFUL, CHILDREN...YE'VE CAUSED ME A BARREL O' TROUBLE-- BUT COME QUIETLY NOW, SURRENDER YER GUNS AN' YER WOMEN, AN' WE'LL SAY NO MORE ABOUT IT...

YE WILL LIVE, CHILDREN... YE'VE CASTENADO'S WORD ON THAT...

Y'ALL HEAR THIS?!

GET THEE BEHIND ME, SATAN!!

OH DEAR.

TO BE CONCLUDED!

Part Five:

Pilgrim's Progress

Garth Ennis
Creator/Writer

Carlos Ezquerra
Creator/Artist

Paul Mounts
Colors

Chris Eliopoulos
Letters

Jimmy Palmiotti
Editor

Gareb S. Shamus
Chairman

Fred Pierce
President & COO

AAAAAAHHH!!

LOOK TO YORE FRONT! LEAVE THE FALLEN, THERE AIN'T NO HELPIN' 'EM NOW! TAKE COMFORT INSTEAD IN THE WORDS O' THE PSALMS--

"THOU PREPAREST A TABLE FOR ME IN THE PRESENCE O' MINE ENEMIES!"

YEA, THOUGH I WALK THROUGH THE VALLEY O' THE SHADOW O' DEATH, I WILL FEAR NO EVIL!

FOR THOU ART WITH ME! THY ROD AN' THY STAFF, THEY COMFORT ME!

"THOU ANOINTEST MY HEAD WITH OIL!"

"MY CUP RUNNETH OVER!!"

105

107

HNNH--!

WELL, SAUL HATH SLAIN HIS THOUSANDS.

AN' DAVID HIS TENS OF THOUSANDS.

YOU TOTAL BLOODY BASTARD!!

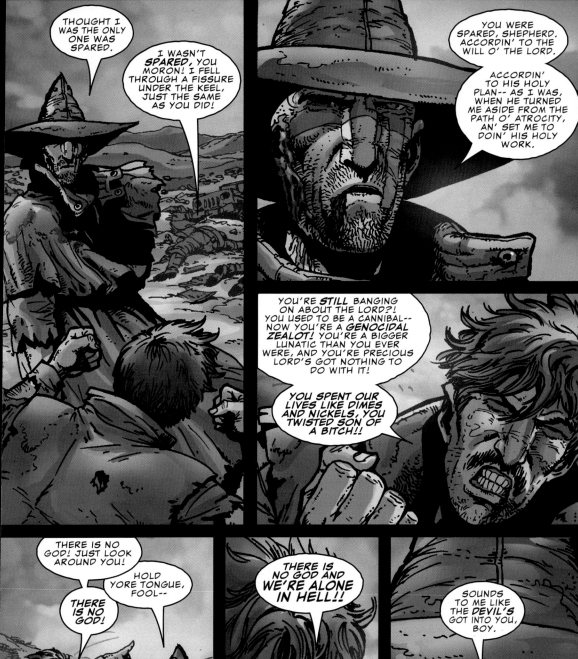

THOUGHT I WAS THE ONLY ONE WAS SPARED.

I WASN'T **SPARED**, YOU **MORON!** I FELL THROUGH A FISSURE UNDER THE KEEL, JUST THE SAME AS YOU DID!

YOU WERE SPARED, SHEPHERD. ACCORDIN' TO THE WILL O' THE LORD.

ACCORDIN' TO HIS HOLY PLAN-- AS I WAS, WHEN HE TURNED ME ASIDE FROM THE PATH O' ATROCITY, AN' SET ME TO DOIN' HIS HOLY WORK.

YOU'RE **STILL** BANGING ON ABOUT THE LORD?! YOU USED TO BE A CANNIBAL-- NOW YOU'RE A **GENOCIDAL ZEALOT!** YOU'RE A BIGGER LUNATIC THAN YOU EVER WERE, AND YOU'RE PRECIOUS LORD'S GOT NOTHING TO DO WITH IT!

YOU SPENT OUR LIVES LIKE DIMES AND NICKELS, YOU TWISTED SON OF A BITCH!!

THERE IS NO GOD! JUST LOOK AROUND YOU!

HOLD YORE TONGUE, FOOL--

THERE IS NO GOD!

SHEPHERD--

THERE IS NO GOD AND **WE'RE ALONE IN HELL!!**

SOUNDS TO ME LIKE THE **DEVIL'S** GOT INTO YOU, BOY.

LUCKY I SAW IT IN TIME.

YOU-- YOU-- BASTARD--!

FORGIVE HIM, LORD.

YOU BASSSSTAAARRD

HE KNOWS NOT WHAT HE'S SAYIN'.

CARLOS EZQUERRA'S
PILGRIM
SKETCHES

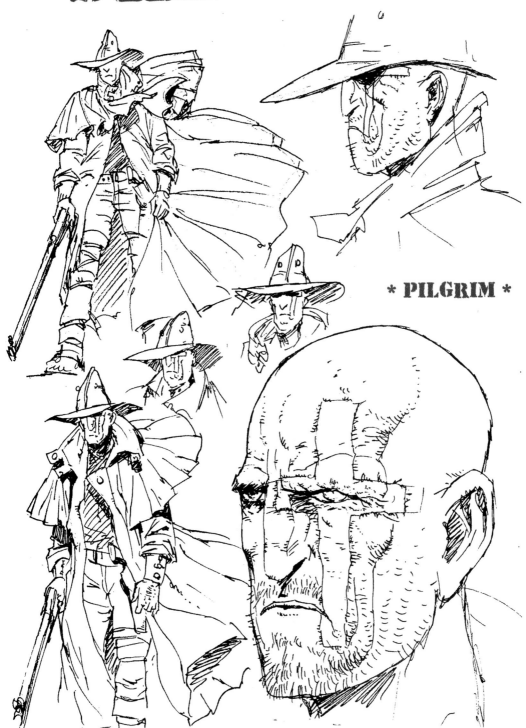

* PILGRIM *

* CASTENADO *

JOHN
* SHEPHERD *

* DIRK *

BILLY
* SHEPHERD *

* PIRATES *

Black sky fade to burning orange

Menacing orange sun →

Pilgrim's Blind eye w/ cross-scar juxtaposed on sky

← OLD SHIP-WRECK

Pilgrin in silhouet shipwre on dry seabed in bkgrn

* **PRELIMINARY COVER
SKETCHES FOR JUST A PILGRIM #1**

JUST A PILGRIM #1 Pin-Up Art
by Amanda Conner

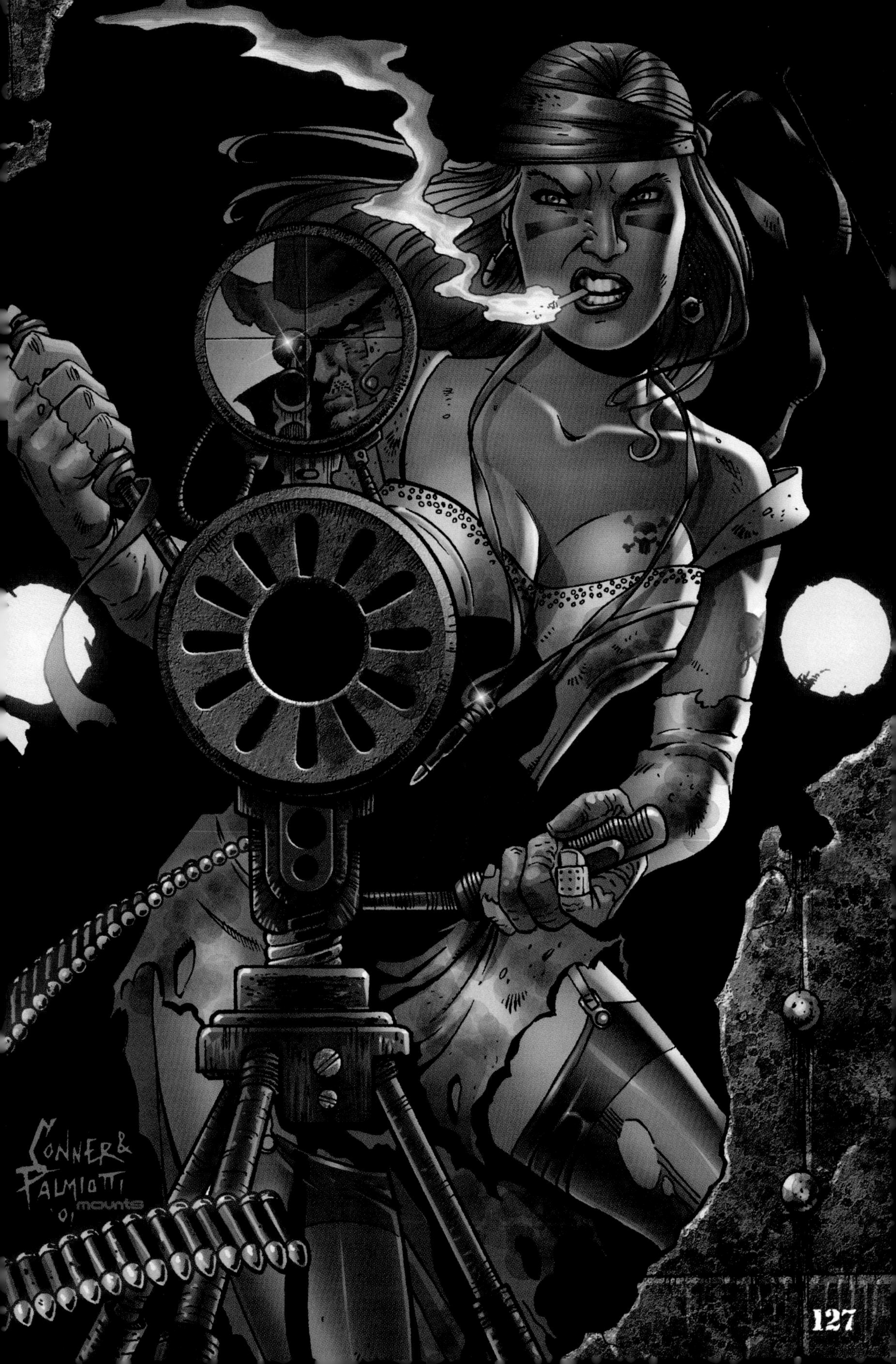

"OH YEAH? WELL ME AN' THE LORD, WE GOT AN UNDERSTANDING."

JOHN BELUSHI AS JAKE BLUES, *THE BLUES BROTHERS*